ACE
LIGHTNING ™

YEARBOOK 2003

LOG IN —

GAME START

CONTENTS

6   The Game Begins... Part One
8   Code Breaker
11   Code Challenge
12   The Inside Story
14   Ace Lightning
16   Curfew Countdown
18   Ace Art Action
20   The Game Begins... Part Two
22   Chuck's Brief History
     of Computer Games
24   Lord Fear
26   Coded Message T-Shirt
28   We Want You!
30   Mark Hollander
32   Game On!
34   Hide and Seek
35   Lady Illusion

36   The Power of Illusion
38   Sparx
39   Tricky Teasers
40   Good, Bad or Ugly?
42   The Game Begins... Part Three
44   Take Over!
46   Dirty Rat
47   Googler
48   Making Magic
50   Friends Like These
52   The Game Begins... Part Four
54   Pigface
55   Anvil
56   The Game Begins... Part Five
58   Cheseborough's Challenge
60   Random Virus
62   On the Trail

Log on to page 46

Log on to page 47

Log on to page 35

Log on to page 24

Log on to page 55

Log on to page 54

Log on to page 38

Log on to page 14

Log on to page 30

Log on to page 60

Log on to page 50

Log on to page 50

Log on to page 50

Log on to page 50

Pay attention! There will be a quiz!

First published in 2002 by BBC Worldwide Ltd
Woodlands, 80 Wood Lane, London W12 0TT

ISBN 0 563 53235 1

Text by Paddy Hempshall

Illustrations by Mike Bowden, coloured by Alan Craddock

Pages 48/49 Photography and computer generated images by Calibre Digital Images

Text, design and illustrations © 2002 BBC Worldwide Ltd

Ace Lightning characters and logo © & ™ BBC 2001

© BBC Worldwide 2002

Ace Lightning is a BBC/AAC Kids co-production

Printed and bound in Belgium

CODE BREAKER

Lightning Knights need to be able to talk to each other in secret, so we have a code.

Here's a handy booklet — the Lightning Knight Code System — that you can take with you wherever you go and keep in touch.

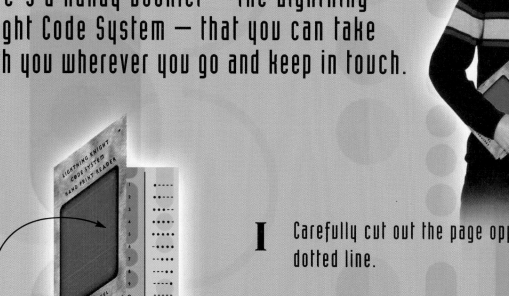

I Carefully cut out the page opposite along the dotted line.

2 Then fold the page in half along the folding line to make a booklet.

3 There are some secret coded messages at the bottom of the pages in this yearbook. Use your code book to work out what they say — you never know what you might find out.

Never let this code book out of your sight. And never reveal the code to anyone except another Lightning Knight — Lord Fear's agents come in many disguises!

REMEMBER: Knowledge is a hero's greatest weapon!

LIGHTNING KNIGHT
CODE SYSTEM
HAND PRINT READER

The following is an approved list of coded messages that you may find useful:

Send help [SOS]
● ● ● — — — ● ● ●

Do right and fear not [DRFN]
● — ● ● — ● — — ● — ●

Enemy found [LFF]
● — ● ● — ● ● — ● ●

Contact me as soon as possible [PDQ]
● — — ● — ● ● — — — ●

Meet me at my house [BHA]
— ● ● ● ● ● ● ● ● ● — ● ●

I have to go [G2G]
— — ● ● ● — — ● — — ●

Over and out [OO]
— — — — — —

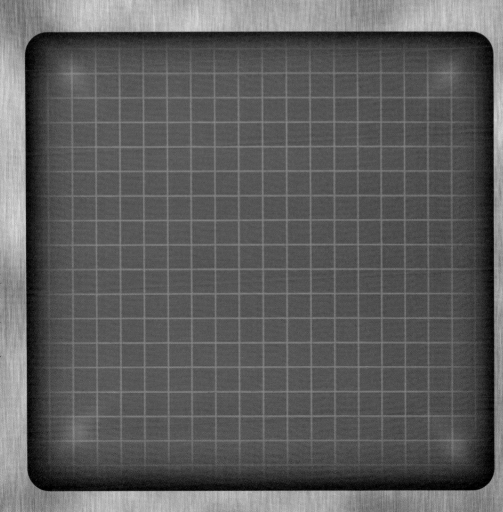

SECURITY LEVEL
⊕MEGA REQUIRED

In the interests of security, all communications must be made in code form. Here is your personal code manual. It includes a full code listing to help you send and receive messages safely.

LETTER	CODE
A	.-
B	-...
C	-.-.
D	-..
E	.
F	..-.
G	--.
H	....

LETTER	CODE
I	..
J	.---
K	-.-
L	.-..
M	--
N	-.
O	---
P	.--.

LETTER	CODE
Q	--.-
R	.-.
S	...
T	-
U	..-
V	...-
W	.--
X	-..-
Y	-.--
Z	--..

NUMBER	CODE
1	.----
2	..---
3	...--
4	....-
5	.....
6	-....
7	--...
8	---..
9	----.
0	-----

Make up your own coded name by using the first letter of your first name and the first letter of your last name. Make a note of it here:

Fold here

CODE CHALLENGE

Use your Lightning Knight code book to take on these challenges.

Mark has left you a message to meet him somewhere, but Pigface has chomped some of it! Fill in the missing letters to find out where to meet Mark.

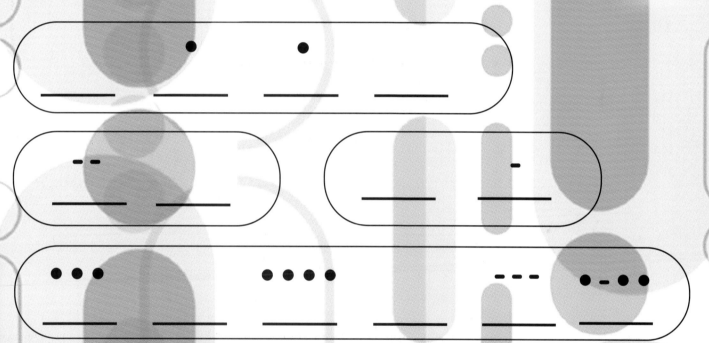

Lord Fear has been trying to crack the Lightning code, but he's made some mistakes. Which of these symbols are not part of the code?

Answers

Mark's message says: Meet me at school. •--- and ---••• are the symbols that are wrong.

11

THE INSIDE STORY

All it took for Ace Lightning and Lord Fear to arrive in this dimension was a piece of the Amulet of Zoar and some lightning. But was it really that easy? We caught up with someone who can let us know: Rick Siggelkow, creator of the TV programme.

SO WHO WAS YOUR FAVOURITE COMIC BOOK CHARACTER?

Spiderman remains my favourite superhero. He's a misunderstood teenager, who makes wisecracks while he's fighting the bad guys. I liked the idea that he had these amazing superpowers, but his personal life was still a mess — which was an inspiration for our lead character, Mark Hollander.

AND WHO IS YOUR FAVOURITE CHARACTER IN ACE LIGHTNING?

I like them all. Among the animated characters Lord Fear and his Staff are my favourites because they are so evil, but they can never succeed with their schemes. Among the human characters, I'd say Mark because he is a solid, leading-man type of character; Chuck, because he is so funny; and Samantha because she's the most realistic character and has such a great personality.

WHAT WAS THE INSPIRATION FOR THE SERIES?

Originally it was a story about a comic book hero that comes to life. But kids now spend more time playing computer games, so Ace became a computer character.

WOULD YOU SAY THAT YOU ARE LIKE ANY OF THE CHARACTERS?

I'd like to say Ace Lightning, since he's the superhero! But, if I'm honest, I'd say I'm a combination of Mark, since I draw on my own experience of growing up to create situations for him, and Simon, Mark's father, since I'm also a father of two teenagers.

HOW LONG DID THE SERIES TAKE TO MAKE?

We developed it for about two years before we started shooting. It takes about a month to finish a script, four days to shoot the live action for one show, three to four weeks to do the animation for that show, and another month to do the music and sound-effects. Because some of this overlaps, it takes us roughly a year and a half to make 26 half-hour episodes!

AND WHAT WAS THE BIGGEST CHALLENGE YOU HAD TO OVERCOME?

Finding a balance between the everyday world that Mark lives in and the superhero world that Ace Lightning lives in. Both the worlds had to be interesting and compelling in their own right, or else the show wouldn't hold together. Another big challenge was blending the liveaction and the animation so that it looked seamless and natural.

SO WHAT DO YOU THINK PEOPLE WILL LIKE MOST ABOUT ACE LIGHTNING?

Ace Lightning really has three strong elements: the action, where Ace battles the bad guys; the humour, where Mark tries to cope with having a superhero in his life and the antics of his friend Chuck; and the relationships between the kids as they struggle with things in their lives like doing homework, getting along with parents, going out on dates and so on.

13

ACE LIGHTNING

Ace Lightning is the only thing standing between our dimension and slavery at the hands of Lord Fear. But what do we really know about this brave Lightning Knight?

Ace has the power of lightning at his fingertips — literally!
His main weapons are lightning bolts which he can fire from his fists!

He also has the ability to fly at high speeds.

But his powers come at a cost. Ace must recharge himself regularly or he will weaken and disappear!

Ace and Lord Fear go back a long way — how do you think Lord Fear got that limp?

Above all, Ace is a true superhero. That's because he's programmed that way!

ACE LIGHTNING

AGE: 76 Kyrilian cycles (32 Earth years).

POWERS: Lightning bolts and flight.

ENEMIES: Lord Fear and the evil gang.

FAVOURITE SAYING: "Do right and fear not!"

CURFEW COUNTDOWN

Mark is in a real hurry! He's been helping Ace save the world, but has to get back to his house before curfew. Grab a dice, a pencil and a counter and see if you can get him home in time.

Put a cross in a blue box on the opposite page for every square you move. If you fill them all in before Mark gets home, then he's late and in real trouble!

2

1

START

3

4

+EACHER WI+H CLASS

Mr Cheseborough makes you retake a test. Fill in two more boxes.

Hitch a lift with Sparx. Fill in one extra box, and move to number 17.

15

14

13

16

17

18

Lady Illusion uses a smoke bomb to blind you. Fill in two extra boxes while you try to find your way.

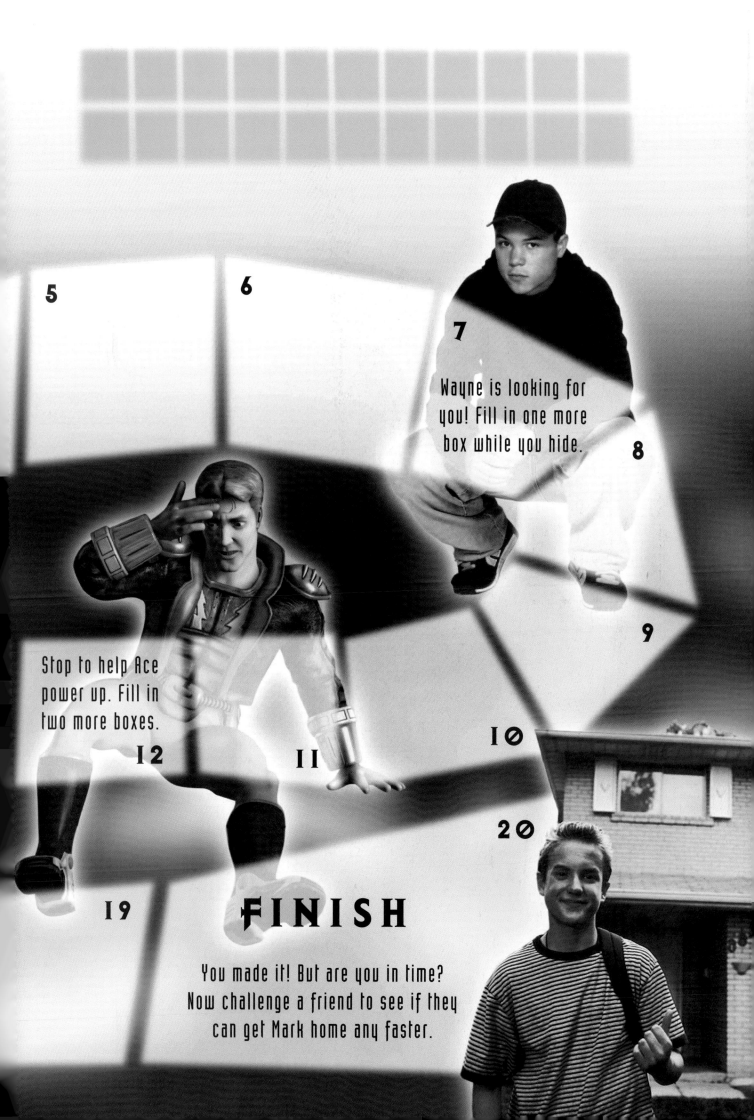

5

6

7

Wayne is looking for you! Fill in one more box while you hide.

8

9

Stop to help Ace power up. Fill in two more boxes.

12

11

10

19

20

FINISH

You made it! But are you in time? Now challenge a friend to see if they can get Mark home any faster.

ACE ART ACTION

Ever wanted to be able to draw your own superheroes? Follow our simple guide and you can start by learning how to draw an all-action Ace Lightning.

I Draw Ace's body as a series of shapes.

2 Draw Ace's outline around the shapes. Then rub out the shapes.

3 Draw on Ace's face, hair, ears and clothes. Rub out any extra lines.

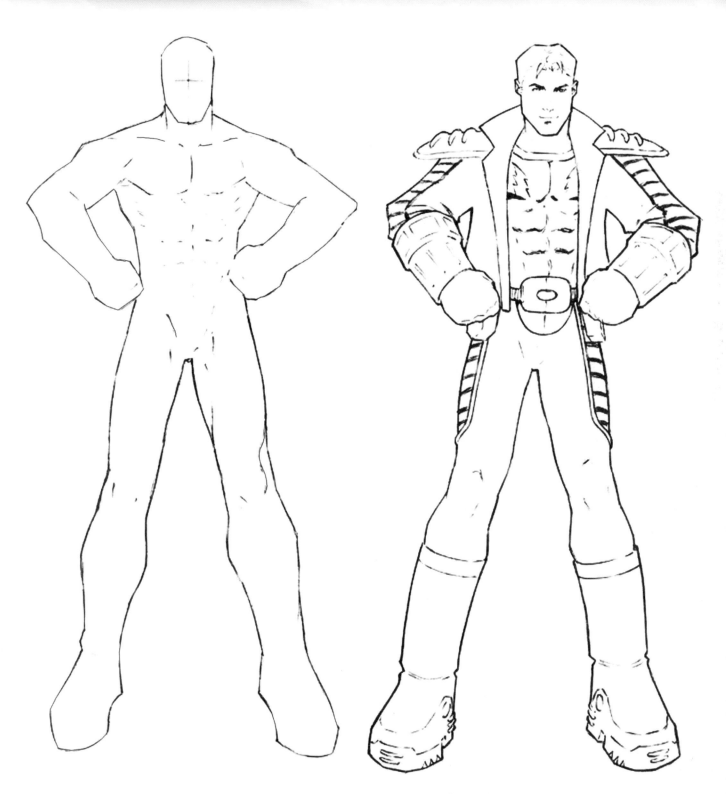

4 Colour in the picture.

We left our hero, Ace Lightning, at the mercy of Lord Fear...

Destroy him! Get on with it!

But suddenly...

Hey! Leave him alone!

Another Lightning Knight? We must retreat and learn more about this dimension.

Mark hurries down to the garden to help the fallen stranger.

Look, kid, if you're going to be my sidekick, you'll have to work on your timing.

Back at Mark's House...

Mark! We're home!

Chuck's Brief History of Computer Games

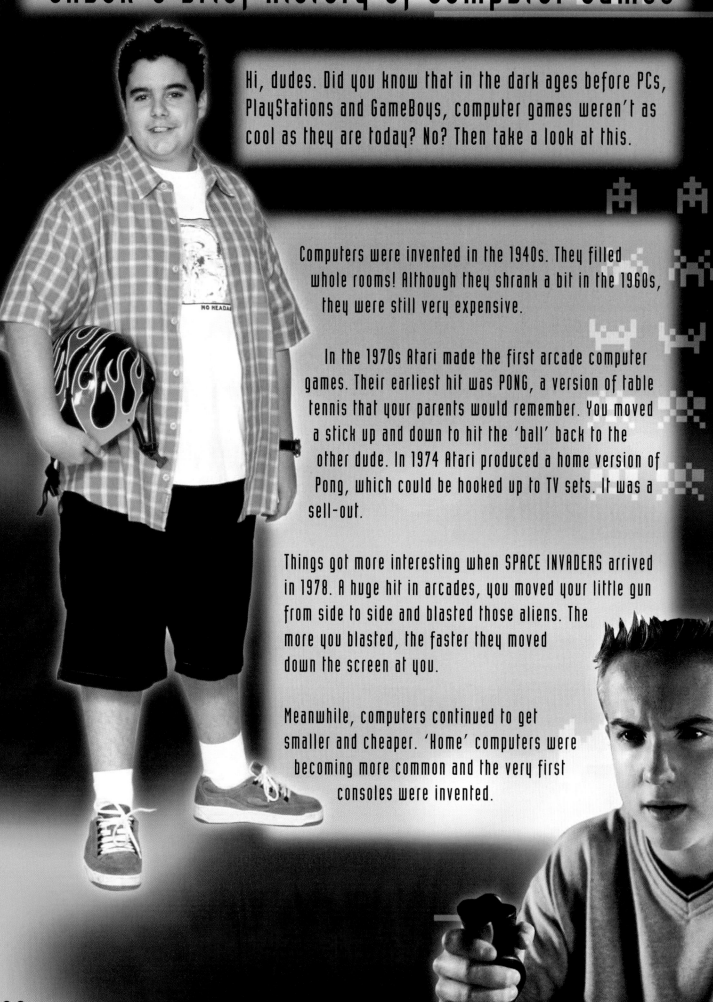

Hi, dudes. Did you know that in the dark ages before PCs, PlayStations and GameBoys, computer games weren't as cool as they are today? No? Then take a look at this.

Computers were invented in the 1940s. They filled whole rooms! Although they shrank a bit in the 1960s, they were still very expensive.

In the 1970s Atari made the first arcade computer games. Their earliest hit was PONG, a version of table tennis that your parents would remember. You moved a stick up and down to hit the 'ball' back to the other dude. In 1974 Atari produced a home version of Pong, which could be hooked up to TV sets. It was a sell-out.

Things got more interesting when SPACE INVADERS arrived in 1978. A huge hit in arcades, you moved your little gun from side to side and blasted those aliens. The more you blasted, the faster they moved down the screen at you.

Meanwhile, computers continued to get smaller and cheaper. 'Home' computers were becoming more common and the very first consoles were invented.

PACMAN was a massive hit in 1980. This little game had your parents in fits. You moved the little yellow dude around, eating dots and stuff! And all in glorious colour. Now that's my kind of game.

Nintendo released DONKEY KONG in 1982. The player had to climb up the screen to rescue his girlfriend from a dangerous ape who attacked him with barrels and flames. Friendly! Mario, a hit character in Donkey Kong, soon starred his own game, MARIO BROTHERS.

Meanwhile, computer games just get bigger and better, and the PC games market was growing. Civilization arrived and you could play games at home on a PC or console.

In 1989 Nintendo released the GAMEBOY, the most successful games machine of all time. TETRIS, a Russian computer game, became the reason to own one. You fitted together little blocks that fell from the top of the screen. Sounds dull but it was hugely addictive.

In 1990 the MEGA DRIVE appeared from Sega, followed by Sega's SONIC THE HEDGEHOG, a game that claimed to bust the video game speed barrier!

In 1994 Sony produced the PLAYSTATION, which changed the whole of the games industry and made computer games cool. Two years later TOMB RAIDER was released on the PlayStation, launching the first female star of computer games, LARA CROFT. Now she's sweet.

So that's how we got to today and Ace Lightning and the Carnival of Doom. [By the way, if anyone works out how to beat Lord Fear, let me know.]

That's it, dudes!

LORD FEAR

A cunning and truly evil mastermind, Lord Fear wants to rule every dimension there is — and he'll stop at nothing!

Crippled in an earlier battle with Ace Lightning, Lord Fear must use a staff for support.

His trusty totem of terror, Staff Head, also fires mystical energy bolts, making it a fearsome weapon.

He might look like just a walking skeleton, but Lord Fear can extend his limbs to catch his prey in an iron grip!

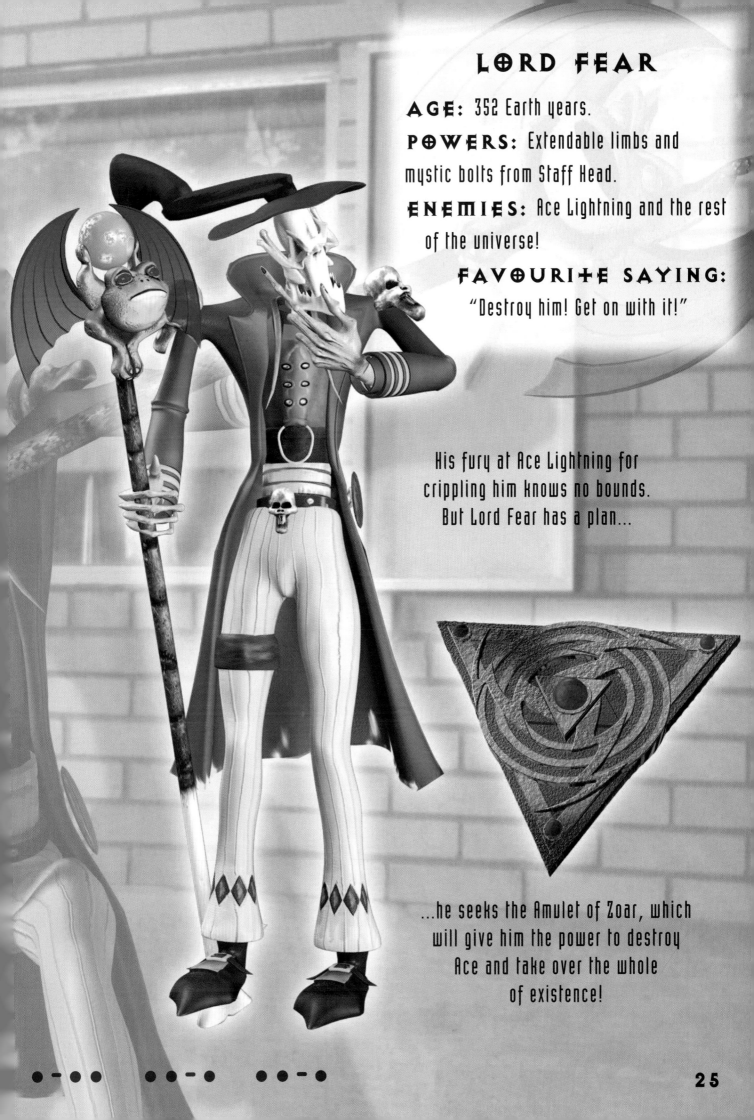

LORD FEAR

AGE: 352 Earth years.
POWERS: Extendable limbs and mystic bolts from Staff Head.
ENEMIES: Ace Lightning and the rest of the universe!
FAVOURITE SAYING: "Destroy him! Get on with it!"

His fury at Ace Lightning for crippling him knows no bounds. But Lord Fear has a plan...

...he seeks the Amulet of Zoar, which will give him the power to destroy Ace and take over the whole of existence!

CODED MESSAGE T-SHIRT

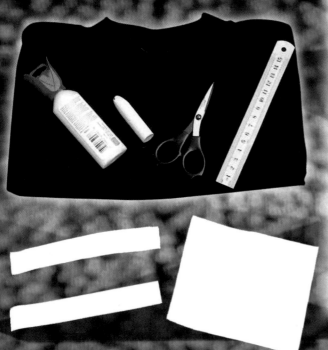

Communicate in secret with friends and Lightning Knights via coded messages on the front and back of your T-shirt. We'll show you how to write "Do right and fear not", but once you know how to do it you can say whatever you like!

Here's what you'll need:

- Scissors
- White felt
- A black Tulip pen (from art shops)
- Two 30 cm strips of stick-on white Velcro (from haberdashers or art shops)
- A ruler
- One washed and ironed black T-shirt
- Chalk

1 Cut out two strips of white felt, each one 3 cm x 30 cm.

2 Using the black Tulip pen and the list of coded letters in your Lightning Knight Code System leaflet, write 'do right' in code on one felt strip, which will go on the front of the T-shirt.

3 Then write 'and fear not' in code on the other felt strip for the back of the T-shirt. Leave to dry for 24 hours.

4 Cut up the felt strips to separate the words.

5 Peel apart the two sides of the Velcro strips. Stick one set of felt 'words' to the glued side of the rough half of the Velcro strip. Do the same with the other set.

6 Use the ruler to help you find the middle of the front and back of the T-shirt. Mark this with the chalk.

7 Stick the glued side of the soft piece of Velcro onto the front of the T-shirt, and the other onto the back.

8 Now you are ready to attach the Velcro strips with the coded message to your T-shirt and wear it.

[The T-shirt can be washed after 72 hours.]

27

WE WANT YOU!

Ever wanted to make a difference? Do you think you have what it takes to be an inter-dimensional guardian? Then take our simple test and see if you could make it as a Lightning Knight.

There are all kinds of heroes out there. Are you our kind of hero?

Are you:	Yes	No
Loyal?	☐	☐
Trustworthy?	☐	☐
Brave?	☐	☐
Determined?	☐	☐
Devilishly attractive ?	☐	☐

28

If you answered 'yes' to any or all of those questions, you might be the kind of person we're looking for.

Every Lightning Knight is randomly given a special power. Roll a dice and see which one you have been given.

1   Computer whizz

2   Human magnet

3   Super speed

4   Super strength

5   Lightning bolts

6   Invisibility

So, now you're a Lightning Knight, what will you call yourself?

_____

And never forget the motto of the Lightning Knights. Write it here in code:

_____

If you want to be a Lightning Knight, you need to look the part. So take a moment to design your new costume.

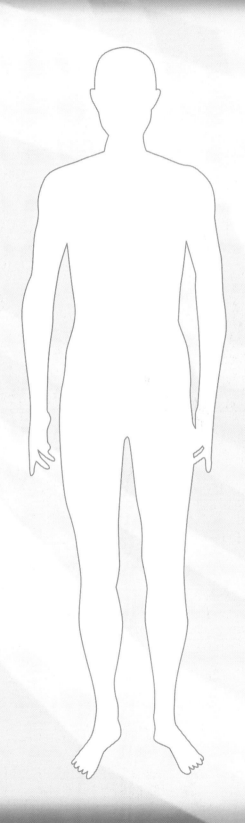

MARK HOLLANDER

He's 13 years old and looking for fun in America. Let's find out some more about our reluctant hero.

Mark is a bit of a computer whizz, using it to keep in touch with friends back home.

And he's no slouch when it comes to his favourite game, 'Ace Lightning and the Carnival of Doom'...

...which helped him cope when the game's hero came calling one night!

Mark goes to Conestoga High School and has put his footballing skills to great use in the school team.

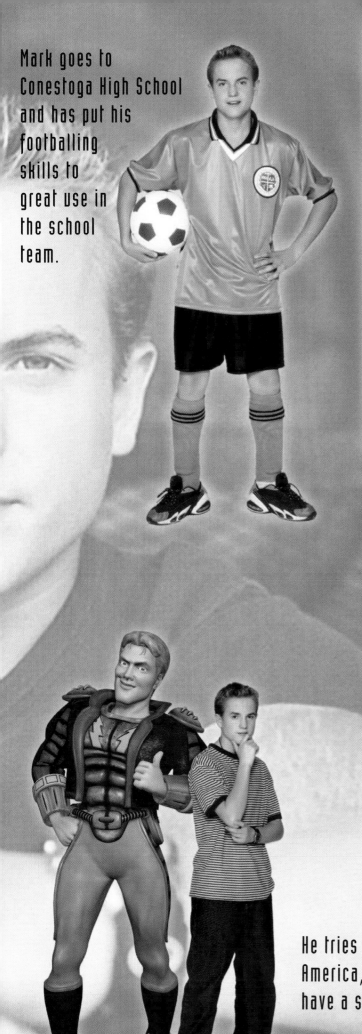

MARK HOLLANDER

AGE: 13

POWERS: A great football (sorry, soccer) player and skateboarder. He also has his own superhero.

ENEMIES: Mr Cheseborough, the science teacher, Wayne Fisgus, Lord Fear and the Evil 5.

FAVOURITE SAYING: "I'm not a hero. I just want to figure out how to get my life back to normal!"

And when he's not playing football or saving the world, Mark likes to skateboard, too!

He tries hard to fit into his new life in America, but it's not easy when you have a superhero tagging along!

GAME ⊕N!

Both Mark and his friend, Chuck, are great fans of the computer game, Ace Lightning and the Carnival of Doom. But what is it about the game that keeps them coming back for more?

EDITOR: So when did you guys start playing the game?

MARK: I bought a copy as soon as it hit the shelves and rushed home to start it right away.

CHUCK: Me, too. Well... I did stop for lunch on the way home first, but pretty much straightaway!

EDITOR: How many levels are there?

CHUCK: We're on number 7...

MARK: Chuck! Actually, there are just a bunch of different 'worlds' to take on. You can do them in any order, which is a great idea.

CHUCK: But you need to beat them all to take on Lord Fear.

EDITOR: How far into the game have you got?

MARK: I'm pretty near the end, but Lord Fear is a hard guy to beat.

CHUCK: You can say that again!

EDITOR: What's your favourite part of the game?

MARK: I love the Ghost Town.

CHUCK: And Sparx is sweet.

EDITOR: What's the hardest challenge you've faced so far?

CHUCK: I just can't get enough pieces of the Amulet to kick Lord Fear's tail.

MARK: The Hall of Mirrors and the battle with Lady Illusion is really tricky, too.

EDITOR: What makes it such a great game to play?

MARK: It's really varied and realistic. I just get sucked into it.

CHUCK: Yeah, sometimes it's almost like it's become part of your life and Ace is right here in Conestoga!

MARK: Chuck!

CHUCK: What, dude? I was just saying...

EDITOR: Anyway, any tips for us beginners?

MARK: Be careful of Random Virus.

CHUCK: Yeah, he, like, totally changes sides all the time.

MARK: Sometimes he'll give you advice which is deliberately wrong. Oh, and as Ace would say, "Do right and fear not!"

HIDE AND SEEK

Mark and Ace are on the trail of Lord Fear and his evil companions. See if you can help them by finding the names in this grid. The names can run from top to bottom, side to side or diagonally.

```
C Y B G L D I R T R S R
A F E A T O O G L A P G
D A D B V O R D T F E O
E P I C Q A X D O Y B O
N G R F I L U S F L A G
V O T Y G D E A O E C L
A O Y A P A R F P C A E
L G R I N U S I O N L R
E L A L L V N S X U X R
A S T O U P I G F A C E
R F A I X O G L S R N C
L A D Y I L L U S I O N
```

LORD FEAR   PIGFACE

ANVIL   GOOGLER

DIRTY RAT   LADY ILLUSION

   ● ● ● ● ---- ● ●

LADY ILLUSION

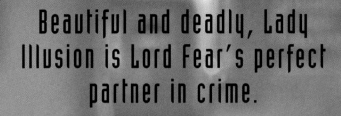

Beautiful and deadly, Lady Illusion is Lord Fear's perfect partner in crime.

It's difficult when she can change into any human or animal form, but don't let Lady Illusion's appearance trick you. She can use her crystal balls to spy on people, or as small bombs!

LADY ILLUSION

AGE: She's not telling!

POWERS: Exploding crystal balls, mastery of illusion and the ability to spy on people from far away.

ENEMIES: Ace (though occasionally she helps him) and the Lightning Knights.

FAVOURITE SAYING: "Just give me the Amulet!"

THE POWER OF ILLUSION

Seeing is not always believing.
Just take a look and 'see'!

Nothing is what it appears to be. Look at
these two lines. Which one is longer?

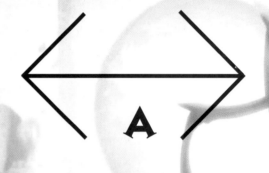

A

B

Fool! They are the same length. Use
a ruler and see for yourself.

The ability to trick the eye helps me hide things
and go unnoticed. Tell me, what do you see here?
Is it really a cup?
Look again. It's two faces...

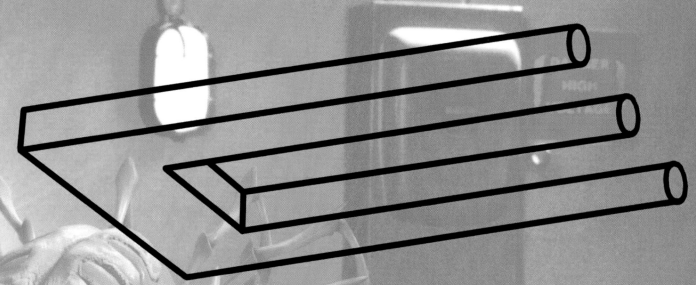

The power of illusion is great. Surprise me and tell me how many points you see on this fork. Are there really three? Take a closer look...

You hunt Lord Fear and his piece of the Amulet. But it is too well hidden... Is there a piece here or have you fallen under the spell of Lady Illusion?

Look at this triangle. Where does it begin? Where does it end? It is useless to try and find the end, just as it is useless to try and defeat Lord Fear and the power of illusion!

SPARX

A real live wire, Sparx, the Lightning Knight, is summoned by Ace to help him stop Lord Fear.

Never one to hold back, Sparx flies into action on a supersonic Lightning Flash.

A deadly fighter with her hands, she can also fire lightning blasts from her weapon, the Sword of Jacob!

SPARX

AGE: She's not telling!

POWER: Lightning blasts and flight. Martial arts expert.

ENEMIES: Lord Fear and the evil gang.

FAVOURITE SAYING: "Let's go!"

TRICKY TEASERS

Lady Illusion has tried to disguise herself as Mr Cheseborough. Help Ace find her by picking out which picture is different to the others.

A   B   C   D

Ace needs to power back up after running into Lord Fear. Work out which battery comes next in each number sequence, below, to find out which socket Ace should use.

Clue: Ace needs exactly 18 volts to recharge.

A   1   1   6   1

B   4   3   4   3

C   2   2   5   5

Answers:
Picture c is Lady Illusion in disguise. The numbers of the next batteries in the sequences are: A1, 44, C2. Ace needs to use socket B.

39

GOOD, BAD OR UGLY?

Who is your hero? Are you brave like Ace or sneaky like Dirty Rat? Do our quiz and find out.

You're walking down the street when someone accidentally knocks your ice cream out of your hand. Do you:

a: Accept their apology and let them buy you another?

b: Insist there is no excuse for clumsiness and melt their brain?

c: Eat it anyway. Then eat them?

d: Consider teaching them a lesson, but then calm down and accept their apology?

What would be your ideal present?

a: Justice for all and an end to evil?

b: Something small, like the Universe, to do with as you will?

c: Something to eat?

d: Something for yourself that will help you to help others?

Your younger brother can't open his can of fizzy drink. Do you:

a: Look devilishly handsome while you open it for him with your super strength?

b: Let him keep trying, because it's funny to watch?

c: Open it for him and then drink it?

d: Open it for him in such a rush that it spills everywhere?

In a shop, you see that someone has dropped their wallet. Do you:

a: Immediately return the wallet to its owner?

b: Make away with the wallet and use the cash to fund your plans for world domination?

c: Eat it?

d: Think about keeping the wallet, but return it in the end?

You've bought a Christmas present for someone, but you really like it, too. Do you:

a: Wrap it up for them anyway? After all, giving is better than receiving.
b: Wonder what came over you that made you buy a present for someone else in the first place, and keep it?
c: Eat it?
d: Think about keeping it, but then buy yourself one and give the other as a present?

You've lost your favourite toy. Do you:

a: Calmly try and remember where you last saw it, and then search the house, room by room?
b: Take over the whole town in revenge for someone stealing it?
c: Forget it and just go for lunch?
d: Ramdomly search the house in the hope that you'll find it?

If you answered:

Mostly a: Ace would be proud. You're the perfect Lightning Knight. A real hero who can always be counted on to save the day.

Mostly b: Lord Fear had better watch out or you will take over as the biggest evil mastermind in the Universe!

Mostly c: Like Pigface, you're always thinking with your stomach. That's if you're not eating long enough to think at all!

Mostly d: Just like Sparx, you're not perfect but you try to do the right thing. Sometimes you act before you think, but you're still one of the good guys.

41

Carnival owner, Duff Kent, has found himself in deep trouble with the evil escapees from the sixth dimension.

Smash! Anvil Smash him!

NO! You are never to harm this gentleman without my permission.

Uh, n-n-now I think of it, I could use some help. You're all hired!

Splendid! I trust this is the beginning of a most profitable partnership.

The next morning, and it's time for Mark to get ready for his first day at school.

CRAAAAASSSH!

Nap time's over, Mickey.

We have to find Lord Fear and send him back to the sixth dimension. It's our mission.

My only mission is to get through my first day of school. And it's Mark . . . Mark!

After Ace leaves, Mark makes his way to the bus stop and meets his new neighbour, Samantha.

So, you like your video games loud then?

Uh, yeah! It makes it more realistic.

I know. I could hear the voices last night. You must have awesome speakers.

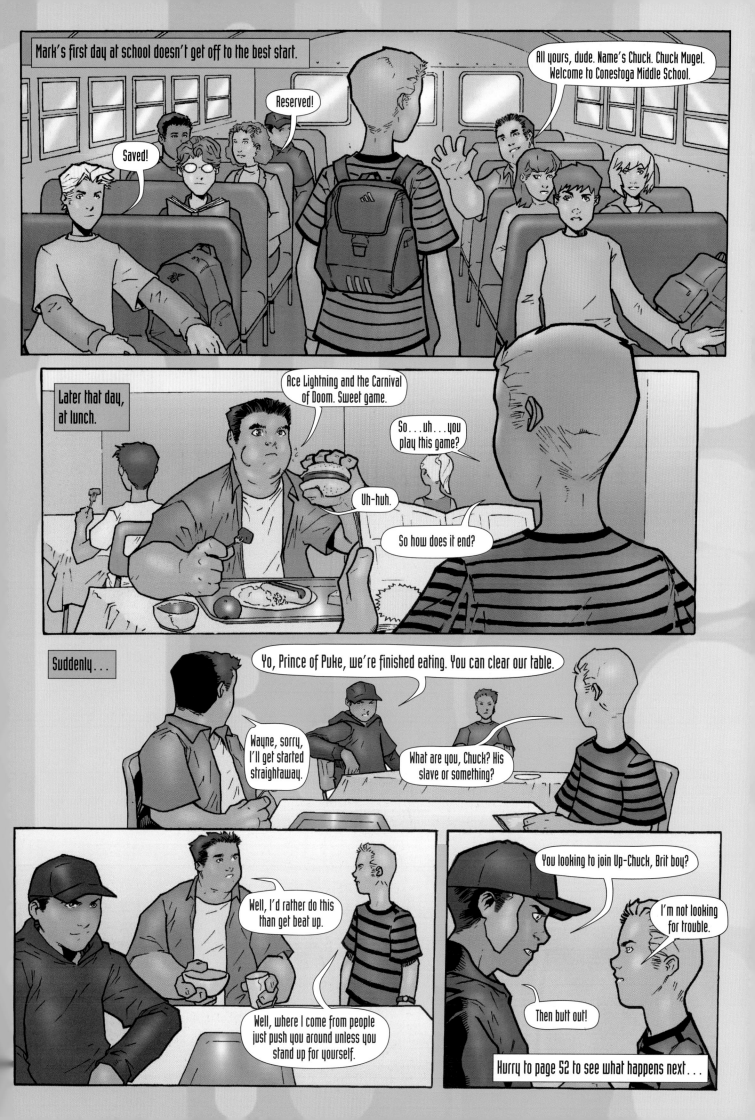

TAKE OVER!

Forget protecting the Universe — how would you like to rule it? We're always looking for more fiendish friends to help take over reality. Care to join us?

"Help us rid reality of meddling mortals!"

Are you:	Yes	No
Sneaky?	☐	☐
Devious?	☐	☐
Full of cunning plans?	☐	☐
Power-hungry?	☐	☐
Sickened by goody-goody Lightning Knights?	☐	☐

If you didn't answer 'yes' to any of these questions, why not? You certainly won't make it as an evil mastermind, so go and see if the whining, muscle-bound moro Ace Lightning will take you!

So what will you bring to our little band? Roll a dice and see. And remember — for a bad guy, cheating is just plain normal...

1	Bad smells
2	Super strength
3	Ability to fly
4	Super smart
5	X-ray vision
6	Exploding trousers

Lady Illusion will let you take on any form you want, so draw something for her to copy:

So, now you're an evil genius, what will we call you?

And never forget — if anyone asks, you've never heard of us!

DIRTY RAT

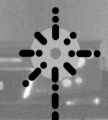

A sneaky creature, his name is well-deserved.

Dirty Rat is Lord Fear's sneaky 'spy in the sky'. He's small and fast enough to fly around and keep an eye on things without being seen.

He can also turn into a stone gargoyle and perch above the Carnival gates as a look-out.

Dirty Rat can hypnotize people and mess with their memories!

DIRTY RAT

AGE: Older than he looks.

POWERS: Hypnotism, flight and a keen sense of smell!

ENEMIES: Mark and Ace Lightning.

FAVOURITE SAYING: "Great plan, Boss."

GOOGLER

He's dressed as a jester, but running into him would be no laughing matter.

Googler can curl into a spiked ball and hurl himself at his enemies.

His two puppets, Zip and Snip, can also fly into battle!

GOOGLER

AGE: 33 googlers.

POWERS: Venom-spitting puppets and a deadly spike attack.

ENEMIES: Mark and Ace Lightning.

FAVOURITE SAYING: "Prepare for Googlerization."

At the Carnival, Googler turns into an innocent-looking puppet theatre.

47

MAKING MAGIC

It's not easy making a computer superhero appear in the real world. In fact, it takes a whole team of people! Here's how the team worked their magic to bring Ace into Mark's life.

The process of making one single frame of computer animation featuring Mark and Ace starts with a writer, a director and a storyboard artist. The writer creates the script, which the director visualizes with the help of the storyboard artist.

Next, the live action film crew shoot film of Mark, leaving a space for Ace in the shot.

The character animator poses Ace in the scene. At this stage he's in wireframe.

But before the character animator can even start, a model — maquette — of Ace has to be created through line drawings, texture maps and polygons.

Once Ace has been animated, the lighter uses a library of textures and lights to make Ace look like he's really beside Mark.

When all the lights, shadows and texture maps are fully rendered, the image of Ace and Mark is ready.

Magic!

FRIENDS LIKE THESE

When Mark moved to Conestoga Hills from England, he had to make a whole new set of friends...and enemies.

CHUCK MUGEL

AGE: 13

SKILLS: A computer whizz who's great with computer games. And he eats a lot, too!

ENEMIES: Wayne Fisgus, Lord Fear and the evil gang.

FAVOURITE SAYING:
"Are we still playing the game?"

Chuck is a nerd, and he knows it. But the thing is, he doesn't care! One of the first friends that Mark made, he finds out about Ace Lightning and helps fight Lord Fear. He is also known for being sick at the drop of a hat, earning him the name 'Chucky Upchuck' from Wayne.

SAMANTHA THOMPSON

AGE: 13

POWERS: A cheerleading star who knows what she wants — and gets it.

ENEMIES: Not many — she's probably the most popular girl in school.

FAVOURITE SAYING:
"Mark, what's going on?"

Samantha is Mark's next door neighbour. She's a cheerleader and her boyfriend, Brett, is on the school soccer team. She knows that Mark is hiding something and she's determined to find out what it is.

BRETT RAMIREZ

AGE: 13

SKILLS: Star of the school soccer team

ENEMIES: Plenty! Brett's good-looking, a soccer star <u>and</u> he's Samantha's boyfriend!

FAVOURITE SAYING: Unknown.

When Mark replaces Brett as the star of the soccer team, Brett is cool enough to treat it as friendly rivalry. But when Mark and Samantha start going out together, Brett's friendship is put to the test.

WAYNE FISGUS

AGE: 13

SKILLS: A bully with a mean streak.

ENEMIES: Anyone who he thinks he can bully – especially Chuck.

FAVOURITE SAYING: "Wuss!"

The school bully, Wayne makes life miserable for Chuck whenever he can. After Mark stands up for Chuck he finds himself in Wayne's bad books, too.

MR CHESEBOROUGH

AGE: No spring chicken!

SKILLS: The meanest teacher in school, with a nasty comment for everyone.

ENEMIES: His students in general, but he seems to have taken a dislike to Mark.

FAVOURITE SAYING:

"Pay attention! There will be a quiz."

He makes science lessons even less fun for his students than they were before. He's extremely strict and loves to give bad grades to everyone.

Mark and Wayne are not seeing eye to eye...

So, Brit boy...

Just then the school bell rings.

BRRIINNG!

What a wuss!

Where's a superhero when you really need one?

Later, in Mr Cheseborough, the science teacher's class...

And this 'H', refers to what?

TAP! TAP!

Huh?

Let's ask our new student. Mr Hollander?

I'm sorry, sir?

Oh, tut, tut, old chap. We must have interrupted his tea time!

52

PIGFACE

A simple fellow, Pigface is always thinking with his stomach.

Pigface loves to eat. He's a huge, slobbering beast that would love to have you for dinner...

He changes into a trash can when he's at the Carnival.

PIGFACE

AGE: 12 Earth years.

POWERS: He eats a lot. And he smells really bad.

ENEMIES: Mark and Ace Lightning.

FAVOURITE SAYING: "Me smells good eats!"

ANVIL

He's not the brains of the bunch, for sure, but Anvil can still give you a headache.

ANVIL

AGE: Anvil can't count.

POWERS: Strong and mean, but not too smart.

ENEMIES: Mark and Ace Lightning.

FAVOURITE SAYING: "Anvil break him!"

When he's resting at the Carnival, Anvil turns into a 'Test-your-Strength' machine.

He may be strong, but Anvil's just a big baby who's afraid of the dark!

He's super-strong, with a huge iron anvil on one arm.

At the Carnival of Doom, Lord Fear has not been idle...

The trap is set. This time Ace Lightning will be destroyed.

But what about the meddling mortal?

Of course, he too must be destroyed. My Lady, if you would be so kind.

Lady Illusion has Mark in her sights.

Meanwhile, outside, Ace has run into trouble already.

Time for Lunch!

How about a bit of 'light' snack instead?

CHESEBOROUGH'S CHALLENGE

I told you there'd be a quiz. Now we'll see who's been paying attention!

1) In which dimension were Lord Fear and the evil gang imprisoned?

2) What is the full name of the Amulet?

3) In which town does Mark live?

4) Who is Mark's neighbour?

5) How old is Mark?

6) What is a maquette?

7) What is the motto of the Lightning Knights?

8) What is the motto of the Lightning Knights when it is written in code?

9) What form does Dirty Rat take when he is resting at the Carnival?

10) What is the name of Lord Fear's talking weapon?

11) True or false?: Lord Fear got his limp from falling off a skateboard.

12) What is Chuck's second name?

TEACHER WITH CLASS

13) What is the hardest part of 'Ace Lightning and the Carnival of Doom' for Chuck?

14) What is one of Anvil's favourite sayings?

15) What are the names of Googler's puppets?

16) The fact file on Sparx is on which page? No peeking!

17) How long did it take to make 26 episodes?

18) What is the name of the Carnival owner who ends up working for Lord Fear?

19) How many points were there on Lady Illusion's fork on page 37?

20) What is the name of Sparx's sword?

How did you score?

Check your answers, below, and find out how you scored.

0-5:   Oh dear! Did we disturb your sleep? Go back to page 1 and start revising!

6-10:   As we thought, you still have quite a way to go.

11-15: Not bad, but it takes more than that to impress Mr Cheseborough.

16-19: You scored really well — just as we'd expect from a Lightning Knight.

20:     Fantastic! You're a star pupil. Ace would be proud.

Answers

20) The Sword of Jacob
19) Two
18) Duff Kent
17) A year and a half
16) Page 38
15) Zip and Snip
14) "Anvil break him!"
13) Getting enough pieces of the Amulet to beat Lord Fear
12) Mugel
11) False
10) Staff Head

9) A stone gargoyle
• -
8) • -•• • -• •• -•
7) "Do right and fear not"
6) A model that is made to help create animated computer characters.
5) 13
4) Samantha Thompson
3) Conestoga Hills
2) The Amulet of Zoar
1) The Sixth Dimension

RANDOM VIRUS

Powerful friend or deadly enemy, Random Virus is all of that and more.

Part man and part machine, Random Virus is a mixed-up hero. You never know whether his good or bad side is in control — making him very unpredictable.

RANDOM VIRUS

AGE: Human part — 35 Earth years, machine parts — 6 Earth years.

POWERS: Amazing strength and the ability to control machiner

ENEMIES: It depends what mood he's in!

FAVOURITE SAYING: "Friendship is for cowards! I have no friends."

ACE LIGHTNING ™

LOOK OUT FOR THIS AWESOME RANGE OF ACE LIGHTNING BOOKS, GAMES, VIDEO AND DVD FROM BBC WORLDWIDE.

BOOKS

Ace Lightning Activity Book

Can you help Ace Lightning save the world from Lord Fear and his gruesome gang? You'll need a cool head and a steady hand to solve the puzzles, unlock the codes and answer the questions.

Ace Lightning Official Guide Book

All the official info you need about Ace, the Sixth Dimension and the race to find the missing pieces of the Amulet of Zoar are crammed inside this official guide. Are you ready for the most explosive battle of your life?

Ace Lightning videos, episodes 1-3 and 4-7 (series one)

Mark Hollander is finding it hard enough to fit into his new American school. But when a burst of lightning transposes the evil Lord Fear and his cronies from a computer game into the real world, life suddenly gets a lot more complicated. Can Mark and the hero of the game, Ace Lightning, stop Lord Fear and save the world? A combination of real-life action and stunning computer graphics, this is an adventure that blurs the boundaries between games and reality.

VIDEO & DVD

Ace Lightning DVD, episodes 1-7

Containing all the action and adventure of the video, the DVD also features animated menus, fantastic 3D and live action character biographies, additional footage and a shoot-the-bad-guy DVD game.

GAMES

Ace Lightning games

You are Ace Lightning — foremost of the Lightning Knights! Dare to enter the sinister Carnival of Doom to find and defeat Lord Fear and his evil band and return them to prison in the Sixth Dimension!

- First person action adventure game.
- Multiple worlds including a Ghost Town, Fun Park, Circus and House of Horror. Plus, a final encounter with Lord Fear in the Haunted House.
- Multiple levels in each world with 3 different skill levels.

⊕N THE TRAIL

Ace is on the trail of a piece of the Amulet of Zoar. Throughout the book there are clues to its hiding place. To reveal them, first answer the questions, below, then match the answers to the Grid Reference list and finally use the four grid references you find there to locate the Amulet on the map, opposite.

WORK OUT THE ANSWERS TO THESE QUESTIONS AND WRITE THEM IN THE ANSWER BOXES.

The number of symbols on page 11 that were not part of the Lightning Knight code.

Twice the number of names you had to find on page 34.

Take a close look at the code message on page 15.

The voltage of the next battery in the sequence that Ace needed to use to recharge on page 39.

ANSWERS

GRID REF 1

GRID REF 2

GRID REF 3

GRID REF 4

NEXT TO EACH NUMBER, BELOW, IS A GRID REFERENCE. MATCH YOUR ANSWERS TO THESE NUMBERS AND WRITE THE GRID REFERENCES YOU FIND IN THE GRID REF BOXES.

Grid references

1 A4	4 G1	7 B2	10 F4
2 See page 34	5 D9	8 D6	11 G7
3 H7	6 See page 30	9 A7	12 A1

Find Grid ref 1 and 2 and draw a line between them. Then find Grid ref 3 and 4 and draw a line between them. The piece of the Amulet is hidden at the grid reference where the two lines cross.

The answer is - - •

The piece of the Amulet is at grid reference: _____